Library of Congress Control Number: 2020909529

Illustrations by Ija Charles
Edited by Armor of Hope Writing & Publishing Services, LLC
Editing team members: Destiny Nixon and Denise M. Walker
Layout design by Garry Atkinson, Fundo Press LLC
Logo design by Tenesha White, The New U

Black Hair Love

by San Griffin

Featuring Illustrations by Ija Charles

Dedications

This book is dedicated to all of my amazing little cousins, I affectionately call generation 4.0. Additionally, this book is dedicated to Ija Charles, a young lady bursting at the seams with phenomenal talent. Thank you, Ija, for believing in my project, **Black Hair Love**, and for the shared love we have for our culture.

Table of Contents

Table of Contents

Masterpiece

Short, tight and wooly
My brothers and sisters rock for sure, see
Popular or unpopular, the regalness
Starts from the natural podium
Silhouette of a neck that gracefully
Displays the most eloquent statuette
Masterfully chiseled in onyx, chocolate, caramel, even beige
So exquisite... no shade

The Trio

Every braid,
Representing the holy trio
Faith, Hope, Charity
You wear it well
As you are propelled, to another level
That many salivate and savor
The holy trio that kept your ancestors during hard labor

Legacy

Locs, long, short, medium
A personal journey we can agree
It's spiritual, it's mental and absolutely physical
Takes thought, takes care... don't you dare
Cut my locs. My journey- my way— my time-
My day. That's what our ancestors would say;
"We will have our day." It's today, enjoy!

YES

Resilient, yes, that's our hair
Resilient, no need to stare
We are constantly cognizant of the resilience in our DNA
And we style our hair and slay in every way!

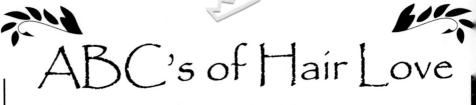

ABC's of Hair Love

Aesthetically Astute
Beautiful, bountiful
Carefully Caress
Dashing Do
Equally Edgy
Fierce force
Genuinely gorgeous
Heavenly hues
Incredibly intelligent

Neurofro

Creativity zig-zag from neuron synapses in your brain

From the prefrontal cortex to the medulla oblongata lane

Thus- manifested through the unique composition on your mane

What's inside is reflected on the outside

Hold your head up with pride- that's how we abide

Radiate

COILS CURLS COILS

Moisturized with heavenly oils.

You were designed to receive,
Intercept the most intricate

Messages   from on

high,

smile with a sigh
Your antenna is built within,
For this you are sanguine!

Melanin Approved

Hair popping
Melanin popping
Skin glowing
Onyx showing
Say it loud
I'm black and I'm proud
You're welcome

Brand New

Handsome
Wholesome
Noble-some
Loyal one
Your hair is second to none
Do whatever you like with your hair
As it grows you can put it in a man-bun
Whatever you do, just have fun!

Blissful Memories

Pinching a piece of hair, starting at the edge,

Grasping all, even a lil' baby hair embeds.

Ouch! You may hear, then a loving, "Be still, Dear."

It may come with a touch, a nudge or a look

Just another page in a natural hair book

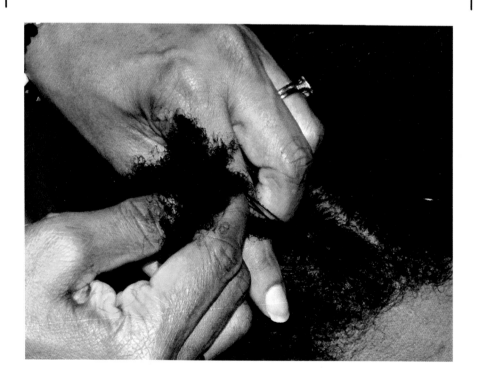

San Memories

Bantu knots

Stresses freshly washed

Scalp clean on a Friday night

You know what I mean

Twist'n and winding

Around that spot, until it's safely tucked in a knot

Wear it up beaming with pride or take it down and

Twirl it to the side.

Retro Thoughts

Silky, straight

Straightening comb

Sulfur 8

Sizzling long

Hot plate

Be still

You'll get burnt

A loving pop

Remind you it's hot

Things we did for those silky-straight locs

Routine Scene

Bonnet, silky and big

Silk scarf, don't you lose it

Wrapped around your head to keep

Your tresses neat and on fleek

A major part of our hair care humdrum

Good, daily habits keep us on task

Also helps the morning routine go by fast!

Trifecta

Water, oil, silk or satin scarf
The perfect trio to kick the hairstyle off
Nurture, maintain, and love
The trifecta result from above
Make it a habit
Make it a routine
At the end, you will feel pristine

Head Wrap Favor

Wrapped, twirled and zapped with love

My hair is protected like hands in a glove

Red, yellow or green, the colors

Not as important as the theme

What it is, What it's not

Black hair is pretty hair

Girls and guys of color you are the definition

Of magnificent beauty

From your round, broad nose, full lips, ancient eyes, and thick hips

To the unique blend of hairs on your head

Knotty hair, nappy hair, bad hair is dead

We reject those labels that brand is no longer viable

We speak truth and what is pliable

People that don't love your culture started that false narrative

"My hair is magnificent" is our new declarative

Black hair is pretty hair, unlearn the false story

Bold warm textures, from super tight curls,

To passive, straight strands; it's all in great demand

Beaming all over your head strong and healthy

Healthy is the best form of wealthy

Thank goodness, for black hair is beautiful hair.

Your Hair is Big Business

Young prince, young princess, listen up

Think twice before you put 7-syllable chemicals on your crown

There's a billion-dollar industry going down

Images floating on media to lure you in

Your hair or skin is not a sin

You are naturally perfect the way you are

Use natural oils and plants from the earth on your body and hair

Defy them, I dare!

Olive oil, water, coconut oil, tea tree and shea butter

Find out what naturally works for you

Your health will excel too!

Don't slather it on your head if you can't lather with it before bed

That's a good rule of thumb

Hopefully y'all stay numb

To the propaganda many succumb

Young prince, young princess, listen up

Wisdom

Jackie Robinson, Sojourner Truth, Harriet Tubman, Martin Luther King, Jr.

We all have the same strain

Mighty magnificent mane...

Our DNA runs valiantly

Be careful not to despise, that which represents you are wise

Boo!

It is vitally important that children of color understand
That which you gather in a rubber band is worth millions
In the enterprisers' hands
Conditioning you to think your hair is inferior
Is an economic blitz to make them superior
Know your power, understand it well
Just don't give it away and dwell
Unknowing, unconscious or unaware
You are more powerful, ha! That's a scare!

You are Powerful

Producer,
Creator,
Inventor
Enterpriser,
Prolific Leader,
Engineer,
Awe-inspiring Speaker,
Doctor, Lawyer,
Scientist–
You are someone great!
Don't wait, shine
Shine now, shine bright
That's right!

Flow

Artistry in motion
There is no magic potion
Just confidence, being yourself
And when the naysayers talk
Be selectively deaf
Let your vibe flow from the inside out
You are true art in motion, no doubt
Creativity, boldness, a glow
What people think of you is irrelevant
So... keep your head up, you are artistry in motion

Haiku for You

Multifaceted

Not monolithic the same

Hence the brilliantness

Dreadlock Love and Respect

Dread Loc Luv

Dreadlocks are so much more than a fad;

They're actually a genesis we always had

Mummies discovered and uncovered in Egypt,

Found their locs still intact

They were pharaohs, to be exact,

Derived from respect

Many people don't understand the sacred aspect

Noted in literary docs in India in 1700 BC,

Dreadlocks are a part of every culture, you see

3,600 years ago, the Minoan civilization, Europe's earliest peeps,

Wore their hair in locs for keeps

The hairstyle chosen by Kenya-Maasai warriors,

Your locs are a multicultural symbol

Of energy, strength, health and immateriality

Freedom personified is the true reality

Rock your Ras, that lioness mane

You don't have to do the mundane.

Scoop-ba-de-Bop

Plaits swinging in the zephyr
Split-ins clipped and dipped
In a little moisturizer
To protect every strand
For the wavy look
Take 'em loose
Watch the defined curls "POP"
Walking down the street
Like scoop-ba-de-BOP
The admiration for my hair is real
The flexibility is a great appeal
Cornrows, box braids, pixie or goddess braids
One thing for sure
Our lineage is strength and sage
Walking down the boulevard
Like it's my stage
Scoop-ba-de-BOP!

ODE to Thee

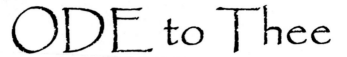

An ode to natural hair; you are convenient and economical
Easy as Sunday morning, you are vibrant yet sophisticated
With baby hair, snazzy lair
Edge up, box cut
Continue celebrating our hair
Join if you care
Happenstance
Research "Crown Act"
No innuendos
But pigtails and hair bows
Tangled, knotted
Frozen in air
Our hair is beautiful
I don't care
Keratinous filaments
Growing from within
I love myself and the skin I'm in.

Born Protected

Swaddled in melanin
Much-needed protection in the sun
Swathe with an afro
To keep your head centered and warm
Born with this awe-inspiring
Armor for security
We are blessed, that's surety!

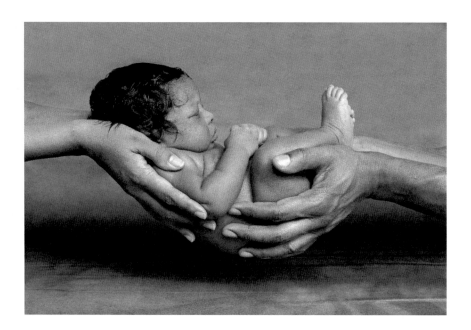

Iconic Black Hair

When you think of famous black people with unmistakable hair,
That connects you to a genre,
A year, a movement, a feeling, a culture,
A political time or an era.
Who do you think of? How about Shirley Chisholm?
Hair as bold and courageous as she was-
With her slogan, "unbought and unbossed," she was the first African
American woman to run for president.
What about Stevie Wonder's braids, cornrows, and beads
Always so lovely, like his hit song?
Oh yea, Angela Davis' Afro-
She was the activist with no activator!
Yea mon, gotta' mention Bob Marley,
The one with the One Love theme,
Made dreadlocks a global statement of love.
Don't forget, Frederick Douglass' natural long, wooly, thick hair was
As bold as his stare
And the publications he promoted to help free slaves!
Needless to say, these people and countless others had iconic black
Hair that defined black history.
Presenting examples of black hair love while impacting socially,
Politically, and culturally.
Iconic black hair-Iconic black love!

Caution

As you proceed through the next half of this book, prepare for the ultimate, **_Black Hair Love_** experience, with profound illustrations by the one and only...
Ija Charles

BLACK HAIR LOVE

Ija Charles

You are the Dream

The tighter the knot
The closer the thought
Your genes are connected to the
Richest continent on the earth
Delicate minerals, gems, and natural
Resources flow in abundance
So does every follicle that oozes
Out of your rich pores on your head
Likewise, is a precious natural resource
Wear Africa's legacy with pride
Don't let other idle opinions override

Transformers

Transcending experience
Physical, spiritual, and cultural right
Cornrows, braids, box or micros
How will I do my hair today
Nobody knows
Streak of blue pins with a golden hue
Nobody has a clue
Inspiration vibrates from within
This is organic to us
From DNA, mitochondria and zen
Relax and enjoy this ancient art form that
Transforms us
Physically, spiritually and culturally, right?

34

The Spirit of the Times

The zeitgeist,
Natural and organic, is revered
However, black hair, natural and organic,
Often seems to be shocking
Pictorials used in the past, mocking
What people don't understand,
They tend to fear
Don't water down your strength
Change...new thoughts are here
Respect all-natural hair
Respect all with no despair
Respect is in the air.

36

Brilliant Shine

Halo
Natural glow
White teeth
Almond eyes
Cheeks raised with a gentle smise
Beautiful skin tone
Looks like ancient soil
Healthy, full of minerals and oils
Thriving in any condition
Overcoming any omission
With ideas, invention and enterprises coming
To fruition
Halo glow

38

Floret

Like an exotic bloom growing from the kiss of the sun,

Beaming with delight as water takes flight

Your beautiful hair is too, a natural unique flower

Growing straight up to kiss the sun.

Be Brave~Be Smart

Warm, thick, rich and dark as night

Your hair represents the strength of your fight

Fight for your goals

Fight for your peace

Fight for your foes

Each glimpse in the mirror of history

Reminds you, your strength is untold

Write your story, write it plain

Don't forget there's strength in your mane.

Beads Galore

Oh, my beads
Forget over the rainbow
You are the rainbow
So bright, colorful with delight
Thread them on
Place them on
Rubber band in your hand
Lock them tight
That's right
Click n clack n' the sound of love we adore
The sound of beads galore!

44

Kingly

Deemed a king with a hair-raising theme,

Strong, tough, and unbreakable seams

Go reign on your throne

The world is yours to enjoy

Exude with astronomical joy!

Ancient Descriptions

Hair as wool, skin bronzed
Holy, righteous descriptions
Lost in plight,
But our hair upholds
The description
Morning, noon and night
Rejoice for the cryptic connection
Hair as wool, skin bronzed
Glowing so bright
People naturally feel
Love and light, SHINE BRIGHT!

Young King

My brother, my prince, growing king
You must master what self-control means
Observe Frederick Douglass, Jesse Owens and Dr. Charles Drew
They were pioneers, at best, who knew
Their hair was hard, strong and course
Like they had to be to help change this galaxy
You're one whether you have a twist-out, flat top or bald fade
Know you have a powerful lineage that was laid...

47

Afro Admiration

"A" is for Afro
Afro puff
Afro ponytail
Afro pom poms
Afro mohawk
Thick, organic and regal
Yes, our hairdos are legal
Ancient, yet original
So perfect it's forgivable

Woke Up Like This

Wake-up
Your hair standing straight-up on top of your head
A constant reminder it's not dead
A constant reminder you are a seed
Hair growing straight-up to the sun, not a weed
But like gladiolus, tulips, and sunflowers
A constant reminder you didn't come on the Mayflower
A constant reminder you are unique and you should adore
Every nook and cranny
Why?
Because you are beautifully and wonderfully made
Tell the naysayers, stop throwing shade

To Box or not to Box

Don't fret, it's hard to conform and fit inside the box that other's built
People's wooden expectations can never tame your natural sentiments
When creativity exudes and oozes from your follicles
Actually, it's an organic flow as ancient as the pyramids and Kwanza River

Sunday Night

It's Sunday night and momma's going to braid your hair tonight for the week

Wash, condition and moisturize, grease your scalp and watch the texture rise

Be still, hold your head up, look down, turn to the side, stop wiggling...

All the warm sentiments momma says

"Ouch," you exclaim,

When momma catches the edges we so affectionately call "the kitchen."

Yea our kitchen sometimes needs a little more love

It's part of our culture, our connection, our tradition.

Embrace these bonding moments for these are memories

Our ancestors and descendants will have in common

Put your silk scarf or bonnet on at night;

Keep the braids and cornrows looking tight.

Before you know it, it's Sunday night;

Now it's time to repeat that glorious exchange.

Truth Be Told

I have Indian in my blood, my hair runs red like
The mud in North Carolina dugs
Cherokee, Sioux or Navajo... maybe Coharie, Haliwa or
Lumbee, no?
All so vital to U.S. History, their legacy is not a mystery.
Big curls, silky-straight, long locs– jet black; it's all fine like
Muscadines, rich in color
Jewels hanging, bedazzled, sparkling and fresh.
Sides dyed and laid to the side
Faded, cut high, cut low, suave and debonair, you know?
Gumby, flat top, retro look, and somethings you just can't
Find in a book
Passed down through culture, community and traditions

54

Heroic

There is strength in my mane just like
Samson and Dr. King!
Untold power that aligns every follicle
Love it
Nurture it
Maintain it
And it will reciprocate
Never desolate it,
Because there is strength in your mane

BLACK HAIR LOVE

56

Beam on

Hold your head up, don't look down

Have you ever seen a prince or a king with a bowed crown?

Let your confidence exude and beam straight through your hair

Just smile if they stare... perhaps you are shining so bright

They are having a hard time adjusting their pupils to the glorious sight

Don't dim your light!

58

New Seeds

Who said your hair is bad hair? Who planted those reckless seeds?

Words are seeds, indeed.

What you believe will proceed the truth, according to self-fulfilling prophecy

Plant the true seeds about your hair

Repeat it aloud and proud; you want it to reach the clouds:

My natural hair is magnificent just the way it is.

My hair is big like my giving heart.

My natural hair is thick and warm like the LOVE I share.

My hair is unique and dimensional like my bold personality.

My hair is coily like antennas that go straight up to the heavens.

My hair is strong like the strength of my ancestors.

My hair is versatile and resilient like me.

My hair is the result of my royal DNA.

My hair is marvelous and others do not define my hair.

I love all of me.

Photo Credits

Front Cover, Mitchell G, Photographed by John Riddick
Cover Design by San Griffin and Garry Atkinson

Page 1 _____And-One/Shuttershock.com
Page 2 _____Ollyy/Shuttershock.com
Page 3 _____Ranta Images/Shuttershock.com
Page 4 _____Viktoriia Hnatiuk/Shuttershock.com
Page 5 _____wavebreakmedia/Shuttershock.com
Page 8 _____Sermsak S/Shuttershock.com
Page 9 _____jazzmxx/Shuttershock.com
Page 10 _____San Griffin/PTMA Stock
Page 15 _____Dean Drobot/Shuttershock.com
Page 16 _____Daniel M Ernst/Shuttershock.com
Page 19 _____fizkes/Shuttershock.com
Page 20, Top Left_____Milton Jr./Aubrey Ways
Page 20, Top Right_____Charlotte Purdy/Shuttershock.com
Page 20, Bottom Left_____PhotoSky/Shuttershock.com
Page 20, Bottom Right_____Algernon B/PTMA Stock
Page 25 Top_____Kosim Shukurov/Shuttershock.com
Page 25 Middle Left_____UfaBizPhoto/Shuttershock.com
Page 25 Middle Right_____Nolte Lourens/Adobe Stock
Page 25 Bottom_____CREATISTA/Shuttershock.com
Page 28 _____In The Light Photography/Shuttershock.com
Page 30 _____Andrii Kobryn/Shuttershock.com

Art Credits
Creations by Ija Charles

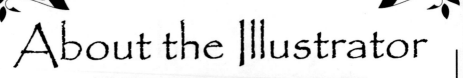

About the Illustrator

Columbia, South Carolina artist Ija Charles is a self-taught painter and entrepreneur. Her series range from portraits of ordinary people to a diverse sampling of symbols from our day to day culture. These images are then reimagined and reconstructed in her own unique way. Ija plants an idea for each new work and harvest the positive vibes her very foundation is based upon.

About the Author

San Griffin, a skilled professional in child development and family relations, has worked with youth and their families for over 15 years. Black Hair Love is her second book, and first poetry anthology, which she plans to follow with more titles that empower, inspire, and powerfully impact readers of all ages. Her debut book is the Amazon bestseller, The Superheroes' Guide to Dominating Their Universe. As CEO of Aggrandize Your Life, LLC., her goal is to provide tangible and intangible transformative tools and resources through the literature and workshops she creates.

San earned both a bachelor's degree in child development and family relations, and a master's degree in human development from North Carolina Central University in Durham, N.C., where she lives with her husband, Milton, and three sons. Connect with her at www.aggrandizeyourlife.com

Special Acknowledgements

Thank you for reading and critiquing some of the poems, Aireaal and Erim. Tenesha, you are always supporting my vision, with amazing logos, thank you! Milton, my husband, who is my first beta tester, thanks for telling me this is something amazing, and believing in my skills even when I doubted myself. My friends and associates, Carolyn, Lashon and Anes, you ladies also read a poem or two and encouraged me to keep going. Thank you!

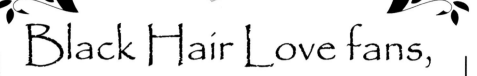

Black Hair Love fans,

visit
http://blackhairlove.redbubble.com
for merchandise!

Made in the USA
Columbia, SC
23 May 2022